Scholastic Phonics

Tap It In

Can you spot the cat on 5 pages?

Published in the UK by Scholastic Education, 2021

Scholastic Distribution Centre, Bosworth Avenue, Tournament Fields, Warwick, CV34 6UQ

Scholastic Ireland, 89E Lagan Road, Dublin Industrial Estate, Glasnevin, Dublin, D11 HP5F

2 3 4 5 6 7 8 9   2 3 4 5 6 7 8 9 0 1

Printed by Ashford Colour Press The book is made of materials from well-managed, FSC®-certified forests and other controlled sources.

MIX
Paper from responsible sources
FSC® C011748

A CIP catalogue record for this book is available from the British Library.

ISBN 978-0702-30866-6

Author
Catherine Baker

Editorial team
Rachel Morgan, Tracy Kewley, Liz Evans

Design team
Dipa Mistry, We Are Grace

Illustrations
Kevin Payne

2

It is in!

Tap it in, Dad.

tap

Retell the story